Volume 3

C000155328

Unto Us A Child Is Born

Words and Music by
Mark and Helen Johnson

Punchy ♩ = 96

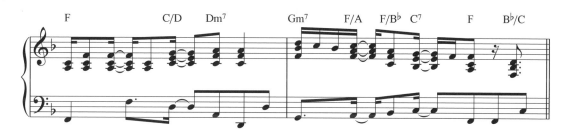

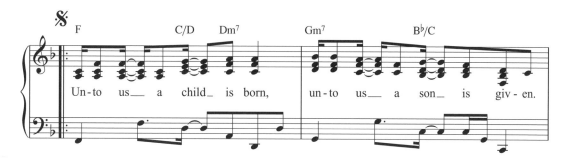

Un-to us— a child— is born, un-to us— a son— is giv-en.

He shall reign in all— the earth, He will be called Im-man-u-el!

Un-to us__ a child__ is born, un-to us__ a son__ is giv - en.

To Coda ⊕

He shall reign in all__ the earth, He will be called Im - man - u - el!

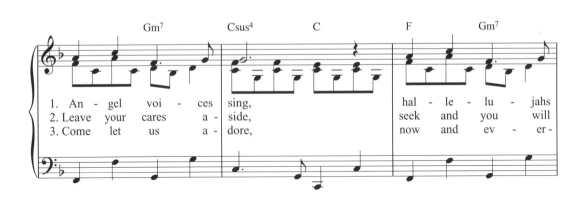

1. An - gel voi - ces sing, hal - le - lu - jahs
2. Leave your cares a - side, seek and you will
3. Come let us a - dore, now and ev - er -

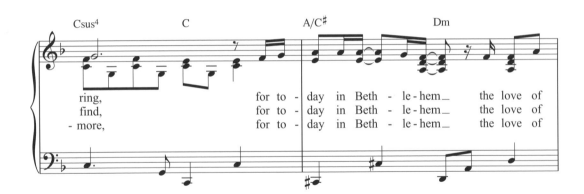

ring,   for to - day in Beth - le - hem__ the love of
find,   for to - day in Beth - le - hem__ the love of
- more, for to - day in Beth - le - hem__ the love of

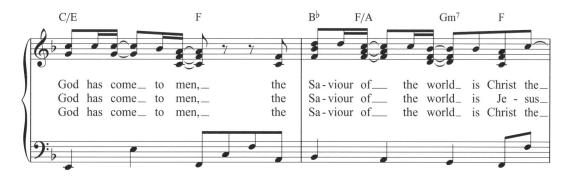

God has come_ to men,_ the Sa-viour of__ the world_ is Christ the_
God has come_ to men,_ the Sa-viour of__ the world_ is Je - sus_
God has come_ to men,_ the Sa-viour of__ the world_ is Christ the_

1. 2.　　　　　　　　　　　　**3.**　　　　　　　　*D. % al Coda*

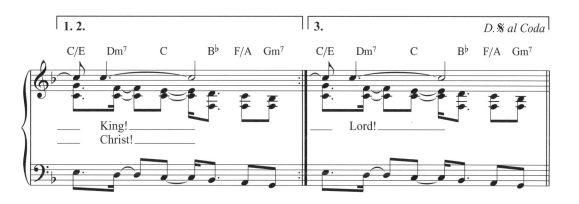

_____ King!_____　　　_____ Lord!_____
_____ Christ!_____

CODA

Un-to us_ a child_ is born, un-to us_ a son_ is giv- en.

He shall reign_ in all____ the earth, He will be called Im - man - u - el!

Hallelujah! Sing Hallelujah!

Words and Music by
Mark and Helen Johnson

With energy ♩ = 136

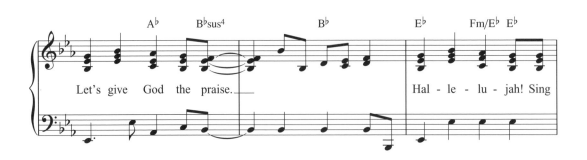

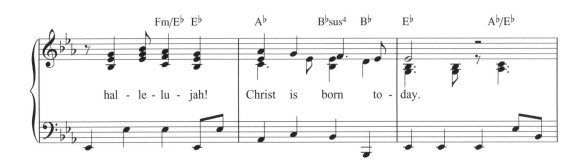

Hal - le - lu - jah! Sing hal - le - lu - jah! Let's give God the praise.

To Coda ⊕

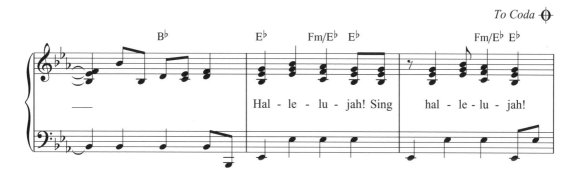

Hal - le - lu - jah! Sing hal - le - lu - jah!

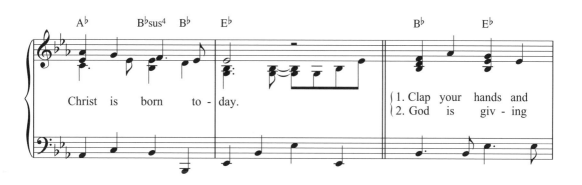

Christ is born to - day.

{ 1. Clap your hands and
{ 2. God is giv - ing

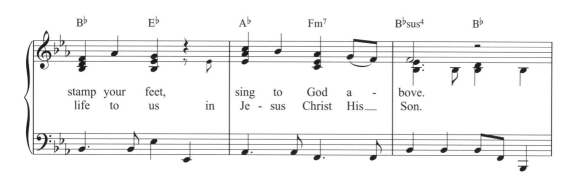

stamp your feet, sing to God a - bove.
life to us in Je - sus Christ His__ Son.

Swing your hips round / to the beat and / ce - le - brate His___
We can come to / know His love, / a new day has be -

1. love!

2. - gun!

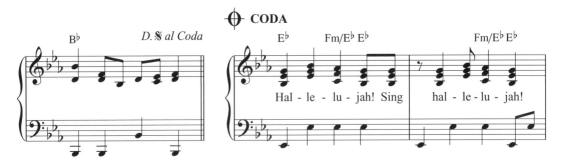

✛ **CODA**

D. 𝄋 al Coda

Hal - le - lu - jah! Sing / hal - le - lu - jah!

Let's give God the praise.___ / Hal - le - lu - jah! Sing

rit.

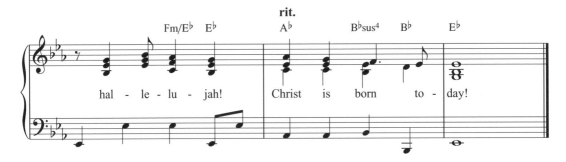

hal - le - lu - jah! / Christ is born to - day!

Christmas Calypso

Words and Music by
Mark and Helen Johnson

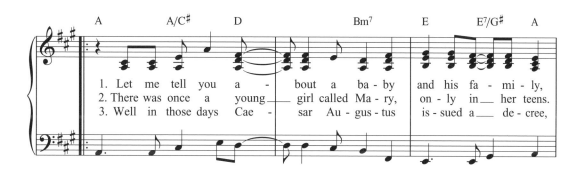

1. Let me tell you a - bout a ba - by and his fa - mi - ly,
2. There was once a young girl called Ma - ry, on - ly in her teens.
3. Well in those days Cae - sar Au - gus - tus is - sued a de - cree,

it is writ-ten down in the Bi - ble
She was vi - sit - ed by an an - gel
and so Ma - ry went with her hus - band

so you might be - lieve.
sent to Ga - li - lee.
where they had to be.

Ma - ny men had told
And he told her she'd
There was no-where else

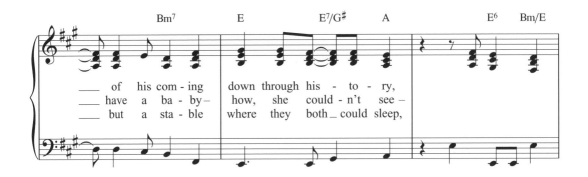

of his com - ing | down through his - to - ry,
have a ba - by— | how, she could - n't see —
but a sta - ble | where they both— could sleep,

now the time had | come— for ful - fil - ment | of their pro - phe - cy.
yet it was her | will— to o - bey him, | so it was— a - greed.
it was there that | she— had her ba - by, | born for you— and me.

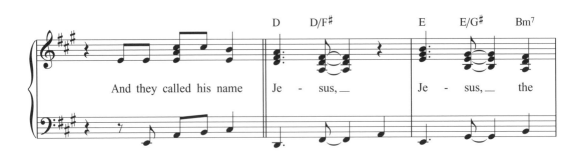

And they called his name | Je - sus, — | Je - sus, — the

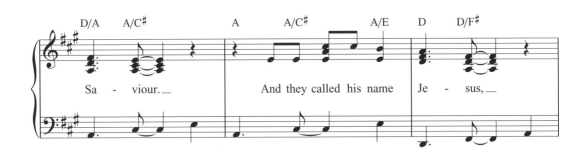

Sa - viour.— | And they called his name | Je - sus, —

Hope Of Heaven
(Christingle Song)

Words and Music by
Mark and Helen Johnson

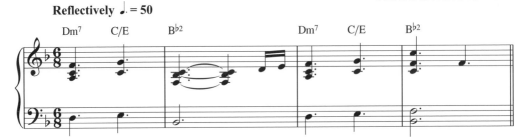

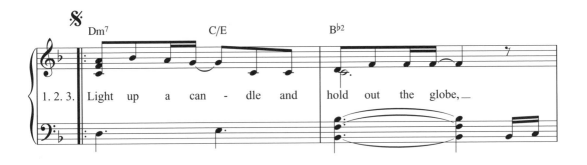

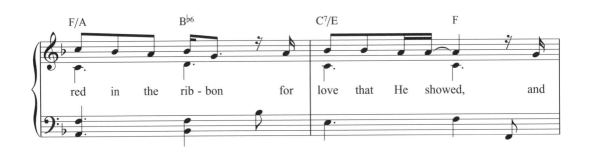

* Alternatively 'fruits' (where grapes or raisins are preferred).

13

The Gift

Words and Music by
Mark and Helen Johnson

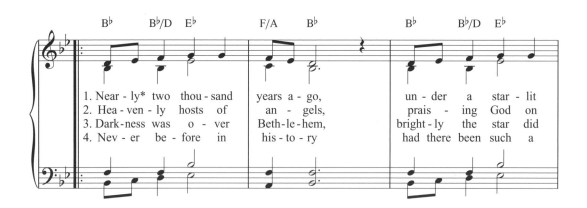

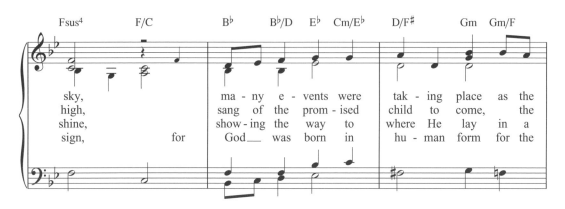

* Substitute 'Over' if preferred.

an - cients had pro - phe - sied.
Sa - viour Je - sus Christ.
man - ger for all to find.

And a gift was giv - en from

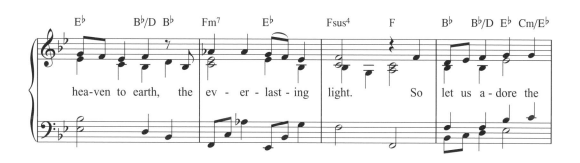

hea - ven to earth, the ev - er - last - ing light. So let us a - dore the

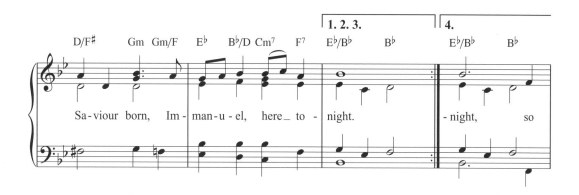

1. 2. 3. **4.**

Sa - viour born, Im - man - u - el, here_ to - night. - night, so

rit.

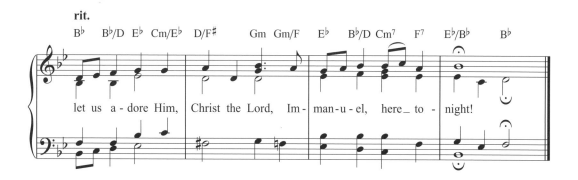

let us a - dore Him, Christ the Lord, Im - man - u - el, here_ to - night!

He's The Faithful God

Words and Music by
Mark and Helen Johnson

He's the faith-ful God, He does all things well,

He's the Lord of all, He's Im - man - u - el!

He's the faith - ful God, He does all things well,

He's the Lord of all, He's Im - man - u - el!

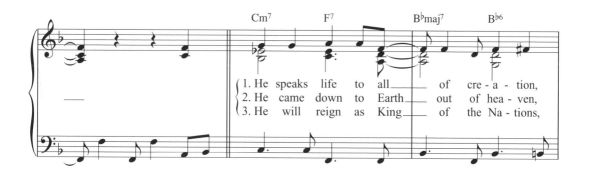

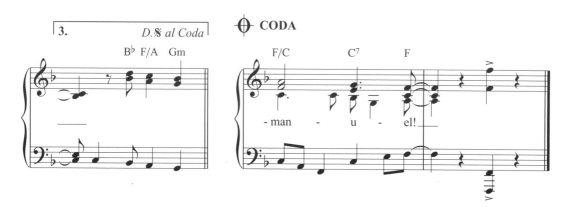

Child In A Manger Born

Words and Music by
Mark and Helen Johnson

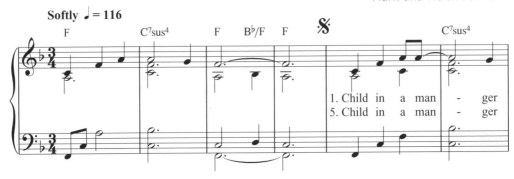

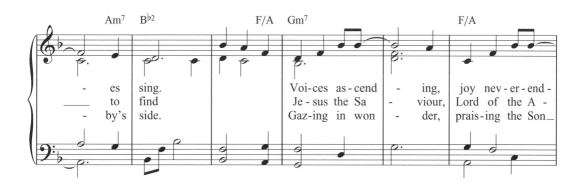

Am⁷ B♭² | F/A Gm⁷ | F/A

- es sing. | Voi-ces as-cend - ing, | joy nev-er-end -
- to find | Je-sus the Sa - viour, | Lord of the A -
- by's side. | Gaz-ing in won - der, | prais-ing the Son

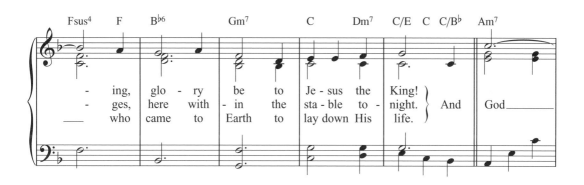

Fsus⁴ F B♭⁶ | Gm⁷ | C Dm⁷ | C/E C C/B♭ Am⁷

- ing, glo - ry | be to | Je - sus the | King! ⎱
- ges, here with | -in the | sta - ble to - | night. ⎰ And God
  who came to | Earth to | lay down His | life.

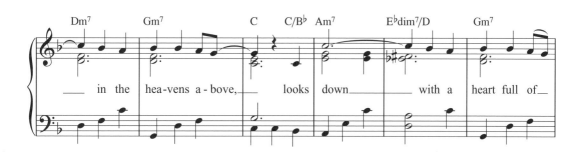

Dm⁷ | Gm⁷ | C C/B♭ Am⁷ | E♭dim⁷/D | Gm⁷

___ in the | hea-vens a-bove, ___ | looks down ___ | with a | heart full of ___

D.𝄋 al Coda

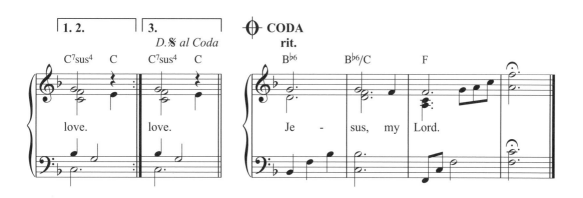

| 1. 2. | 3. | CODA
rit.

C⁷sus⁴ C | C⁷sus⁴ C | B♭⁶ B♭⁶/C F

love. | love. | Je - sus, my Lord.

Father In Heaven

Words and Music by
Mark and Helen Johnson

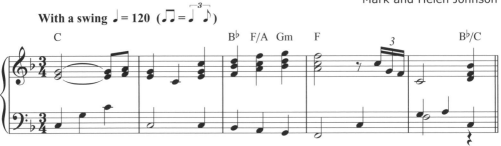

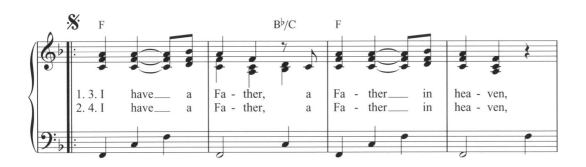

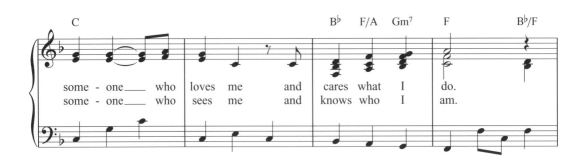

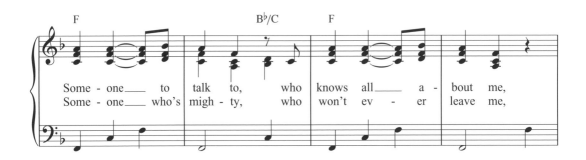

Mighty God

Words and Music by
Mark and Helen Johnson
and Chris Bowater

He Is Immanuel

Words and Music by
Mark and Helen Johnson

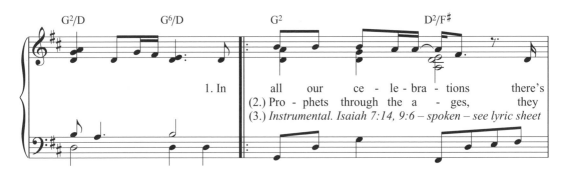

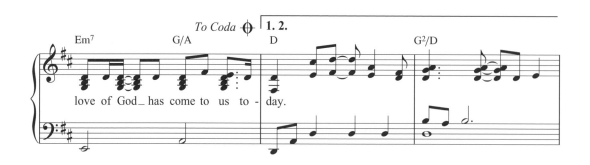

love of God_ has come to us to - day.

2. The
3. Instrumental

- day.

CODA

- day.

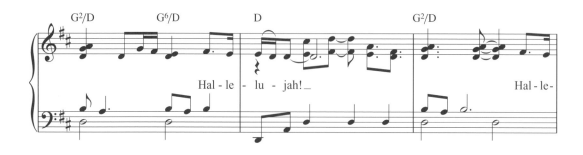

Hal - le - lu - jah!_   Hal - le-

rit.

-lu - jah!__

He Is Good

Words and Music by
Mark and Helen Johnson

Positively ♩ = 118

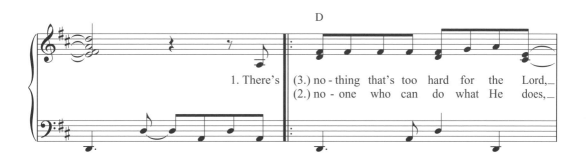

1. There's
(3.) no-thing that's too hard for the Lord,__
(2.) no-one who can do what He does,__

Why Worry?

Words and Music by
Mark and Helen Johnson

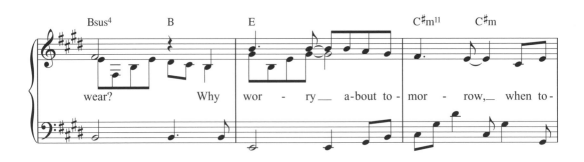

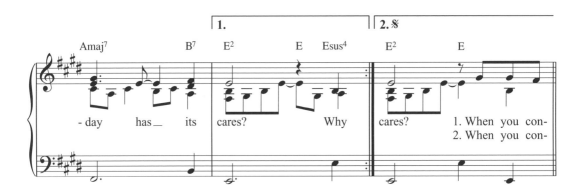

-si - der the ti - ny spar - rows who sow not, yet feed, then how much
-si - der the sim-ple flow - ers whose beau - ty we see, you are more

more will your God in hea - ven pro - vide for your needs.
pre - cious to God in hea - ven than each one of these.

1. *D.%* **2.**

Why Why wor - ry a-bout your bo - dy, what you'll

eat, what you'll wear? Why wor - ry a-bout to - mor - row, when to-

1. **2.** *rit.*

- day has its cares? Why - day has its cares?

35

Unto Us A Child Is Born

Words and Music by Mark and Helen Johnson

CHORUS *Unto us a child is born,*
Unto us a son is given.
He shall reign in all the earth,
He will be called Immanuel!
(Repeat)

1 Angel voices sing,
Hallelujahs ring,
For today in Bethlehem
The love of God has come to men,
The Saviour of the world is Christ the King!

CHORUS

2 Leave your cares aside,
Seek and you will find,
For today in Bethlehem
The love of God has come to men,
The Saviour of the world is Jesus Christ!

CHORUS

3 Come let us adore,
Now and evermore,
For today in Bethlehem
The love of God has come to men,
The Saviour of the world is Christ the Lord!

CHORUS *(repeat 3 times)*

Hallelujah! Sing Hallelujah!

Words and Music by Mark and Helen Johnson

CHORUS *Hallelujah! Sing hallelujah!*
Let's give God the praise.
Hallelujah! Sing hallelujah!
Christ is born today.
(Repeat)

1 Clap your hands and stamp your feet,
Sing to God above.
Swing your hips round to the beat
And celebrate His love!

CHORUS

2 God is giving life to us
In Jesus Christ His Son.
We can come to know His love,
A new day has begun!

CHORUS

Christmas Calypso

Words and Music by Mark and Helen Johnson

1   Let me tell you about a baby and his family,
It is written down in the Bible so you might believe.
Many men had told of his coming down through history,
Now the time had come for fulfilment of their prophecy.

> CHORUS *And they called his name Jesus,*
> *Jesus, the Saviour.*
> *And they called his name Jesus,*
> *Son of the Most High God.*
> (Repeat)

2   There was once a young girl called Mary, only in her teens.
She was visited by an angel sent to Galilee.
And he told her she'd have a baby – how, she couldn't see –
Yet it was her will to obey him, so it was agreed.

> CHORUS

3   Well in those days Caesar Augustus issued a decree,
And so Mary went with her husband where they had to be.
There was nowhere else but a stable where they both could sleep,
It was there that she had her baby, born for you and me.

> CHORUS

Hope Of Heaven
(Christingle Song)

Words and Music by Mark and Helen Johnson

1   Light up a candle and hold out the globe,
       Here in the darkness the light of the world.
       The red in the ribbon for love that He showed,
       And sweets* as a sign of His goodness.
       A life freely given, a love we can know,
       The light of the world ever with us.
       (Repeat)

       CHORUS   *Hope of heaven,*
                 In our darkness,
                 You came to Earth bringing peace and life.
                 Hope of heaven,
                 Full of kindness,
                 Come shine your light
                 In this candle that I hold.

2   *Repeat verse 1 (without repeat)*

       CHORUS

       Light up a candle and hold out the globe,
       Here in the darkness the light of the world.

*Alternatively 'fruits' (where grapes or raisins are preferred).

A Christingle is a symbol used in advent and came from the Moravian church. It was first used in 1747 by a German pastor who wanted to explain the meaning of Christmas and the love of Jesus to his congregation. At this time it was simply a candle with a red ribbon. In Britain, many years later (1968) Christingle services found a place in Anglican churches, introduced by John Pensom of The Children's Society.

Nowadays, the Christingle consists of:
- an orange representing the world with
- a red ribbon around it to represent the love of Jesus/His death
- sweets/small fruit (dolly mixtures are often used) placed on 4 cocktail sticks. These are pushed into the orange to represent the fruit of the earth/the four seasons.
- a candle pushed into the top of the orange and lit to represent Jesus – the 'Light of the World'.

The Gift

Words and Music by Mark and Helen Johnson

1   Nearly* two thousand years ago,
     Under a starlit sky,
     Many events were taking place
     As the ancients had prophesied.

     CHORUS   *And a gift was given from heaven to earth,
              The everlasting light.
              So let us adore the Saviour born,
              Immanuel, here tonight.*

2   Heavenly hosts of angels,
     Praising God on high,
     Sang of the promised child to come,
     The Saviour Jesus Christ.

     CHORUS

3   Darkness was over Bethlehem,
     Brightly the star did shine,
     Showing the way to where He lay
     In a manger for all to find.

     CHORUS

4   Never before in history
     Had there been such a sign,
     For God was born in human form
     For the sake of all mankind.

     CHORUS   *And a gift was given from heaven to earth,
              The everlasting light.
              So let us adore the Saviour born,
              Immanuel, here tonight,
              So let us adore Him, Christ the Lord,
              Immanuel, here tonight!*

*Substitute 'Over' if preferred.

He's The Faithful God

Words and Music by Mark and Helen Johnson

CHORUS *He's the faithful God,*
He does all things well,
He's the Lord of all,
He's Immanuel!
(Repeat)

1   He speaks life to all of creation,
All that lives and breathes.
He's the One who wakes up the sun
And tells the storms to cease!

CHORUS

2   He came down to Earth out of heaven,
Made the blind eyes see.
Broke the chains of sickness and shame
And set the captives free!

CHORUS

3   He will reign as King of the Nations,
All the world will see.
Now He comes with power and love
To all who will believe!

CHORUS

© 2009 Out of the Ark Ltd, Surrey KT12 4RQ
CCLI Song No. 5534982

Child In A Manger Born

Words and Music by Mark and Helen Johnson

1   Child in a manger born,
Lies in a cattle stall.
Safely He's sleeping,
Mary is keeping close beside her baby so small.

2   Angels watch over Him,
Softly their praises sing.
Voices ascending,
Joy never-ending,
Glory be to Jesus the King!

      CHORUS   *And God in the heavens above,*
                    Looks down with a heart full of love.

3   Leaving their flocks behind,
Shepherds have come to find
Jesus the Saviour,
Lord of the Ages,
Here within the stable tonight.

      CHORUS

4   Wise men from far and wide
Kneel at the baby's side.
Gazing in wonder,
Praising the Son who
Came to Earth to lay down His life.

      CHORUS

5   Child in a manger born,
I want to know you more,
Know you are near me,
Love you more dearly,
Jesus, my Lord.

Father In Heaven

Words and Music by Mark and Helen Johnson

1   I have a Father, a Father in heaven,
Someone who loves me and cares what I do.
Someone to talk to, who knows all about me,
Someone who's with me in all I go through.

    CHORUS   *There's a Father in heaven, whose name is Love,
He takes pleasure in showing His care for us.*

2   I have a Father, a Father in heaven,
Someone who sees me and knows who I am.
Someone who's mighty, who won't ever leave me,
Someone whose kindness keeps hold of my hand.

    CHORUS

3   *Repeat verse 1*

    CHORUS

4   *Repeat verse 2*

Mighty God

Words and Music by Mark and Helen Johnson and Chris Bowater

CHORUS Mighty God,
Everlasting Father,
Wonderful Counsellor,
You're the Prince of Peace.
(Repeat)

1   You are Lord of heaven,
You are called Immanuel.
God is now with us,
Ever-present to deliver.
You are God eternal,
You are Lord of all the earth.
Love has come to us,
Bringing us new birth!

CHORUS

Repeat verse 1[*]

CHORUS *Mighty God,*
Everlasting Father,
Wonderful Counsellor,
You're the Prince of Peace.
(Repeat)

Mighty God,
Everlasting Father,
Wonderful Counsellor,
You're the Prince of Peace,
You're the Prince of Peace,
You're the Prince of Peace.

*Optional verse 2

2   A light to those in darkness,
And a guide to paths of peace.
Love and mercy dawns,
Grace, forgiveness and salvation.
Light for revelation, glory to your people.
Son of the Most High, God's love gift to all.

He Is Immanuel

Words and Music by Mark and Helen Johnson

1   In all our celebrations
There's more for us to know,
For plans were made in heaven
So many years ago.
It's written in the Bible,
A story known so well,
Heaven's greatest gift would come,
He is Immanuel!

    CHORUS   *Hallelujah,*
Hear the song of heaven in this place.
Hallelujah,
For the love of God has come to us today.

2   The Prophets through the ages,
They told of what they saw;
That in the town of David
A Saviour would be born.
It's written in the Bible,
A story known so well,
Heaven's greatest gift would come,
He is Immanuel!

    CHORUS

3   INSTRUMENTAL *with Scripture reading:*

Boy: The Lord Himself will give you a sign:
A young woman who is pregnant
will have a son
and will name him 'Immanuel',
which means 'God is with us'.
(Isaiah 7:14)

Girl: A Child is born to us!
A Son is given to us!
And He will be our ruler.
He will be called,
'Wonderful Counsellor',
'Mighty God',
'Eternal Father',
'Prince of Peace'.
(Isaiah 9:6)

    CHORUS TWICE

Hallelujah! Hallelujah!

He Is Good

Words and Music by Mark and Helen Johnson

1   There's nothing that's too hard for the Lord,
He is strong, He is good.
And nothing can compare with His love,
He is kind, He is Lord!

    CHORUS   *Mighty Saviour,*
Great is His name.
Loving Father,
God – forever the same.

2   There's no-one who can do what He does,
He is strong, He is good.
And nowhere we can go from His love,
He is kind, He is Lord!

    CHORUS

3   *Repeat verse 1*

    CHORUS   *Mighty Saviour,*
Great is His name.
Loving Father,
God,
Mighty Saviour,
Great is His name.
Loving Father, God – forever the same.

Why Worry?

Words and Music by Mark and Helen Johnson

CHORUS *Why worry about your body,*
What you'll eat, what you'll wear?
Why worry about tomorrow,
When today has its cares?

CHORUS

1 When you consider the tiny sparrows
Who sow not, yet feed,
Then how much more will your God in heaven
Provide for your needs.

CHORUS

2 When you consider the simple flowers
Whose beauty we see,
You are more precious to God in heaven
Than each one of these.

CHORUS x 2

copyright & Licensing

The world of copyright and licensing can seem rather daunting. Whilst it is a legal requirement for schools to comply with copyright law, we recognise that teachers are extremely busy. For this reason we try to make the process of compliance as simple as possible. The guidelines below explain the most common copyright and licensing issues.

Helpful information can be found on the following website:

A Guide to Licensing Copyright in Schools
www.licensing-copyright.org

And remember, we are always happy to help. For advice simply contact our customer services team:
UK: 01932 232 250   International: +44 1932 232 250   copyright@outoftheark.com

General Guidelines

You are free to use the material in our songbooks for all **teaching purposes**. However the **reproduction** of lyrics and/or music scores (whether for classroom, assembly or collective worship use) and the **performance** of songs to an audience are both subject to licensing requirements by law. The key points are set out below:

Reproduction of Song Lyrics or Musical Scores

The following licences from Christian Copyright Licensing Ltd (www.ccli.com) permit photocopying or reproduction of song lyrics and music scores, for example to create song-sheets, overhead transparencies or to display the lyrics or music using any electronic medium.

For UK schools: A Collective Worship Copyright Licence and a Music Reproduction Licence.
For churches: A Church Copyright and Music Reproduction Licence.

The following credit should be included with the lyrics:

'Reproduced by kind permission © Out of the Ark Ltd'

Please ensure that you log the songs that are used on your copy report. (Organisations that do not hold one of the above licences should contact Out of the Ark Music directly for permission.)

> **A licence IS required by law if you:**
> * Make photocopies of lyrics
> * Create overhead transparencies of lyrics
> * Type lyrics into a computer file
> * Display lyrics on an interactive whiteboard

Performance of Songs

If you are performing any of our songs for the public on school premises (i.e. for anybody other than staff and pupils) then royalty payments become due.

Most schools have an arrangement with the Performing Rights Society (PRS) through their local authority. Organisations that do not have such an arrangement should contact Out of the Ark Music directly. The PRS licence does not cover musicals.

Note: If you are staging one of our musicals or nativity plays then a performance licence issued by Out of the Ark Music is required. This licence covers the performance of the songs from the musical.

Audio and Video Recordings

Copying Out of the Ark Music's audio CDs is not permitted without obtaining a licence from the publisher. File-sharing or installation of Out of the Ark Music's audio CD tracks onto a computer are strictly forbidden. If you wish to make an audio or video recording of any of our works please contact us directly.